The children had some puppets.

"This puppet is Dad," said Biff.
"And this puppet is Mum."

"This is the dog," said Kipper.

Floppy was not happy.

He did not like the puppets.

Floppy barked and barked.

"The puppets upset him,"
said Mum.

Floppy got into his basket.

He fell asleep and had a dream.

Oh no! Mum and Dad
were puppets.

So were the children.

The Biff puppet gave Floppy
bits of wood to eat.

Then the children played with
the dog puppet.

Floppy was not happy.

Floppy sat up. It had been
a bad dream.

Floppy was happy to wake up.